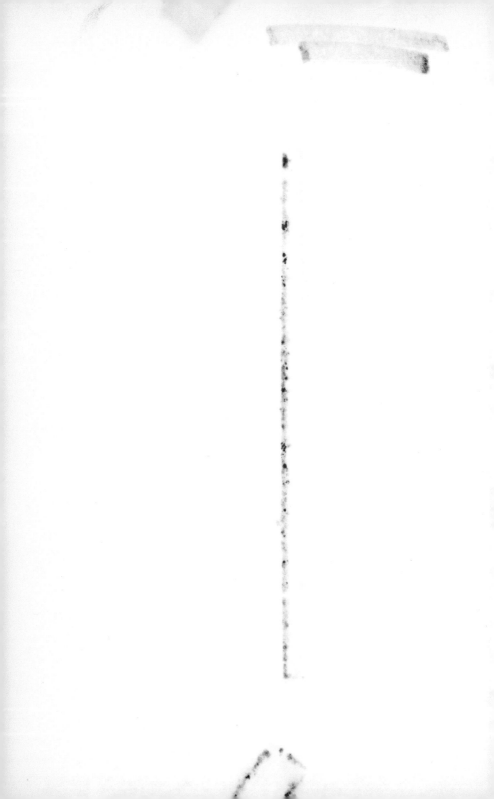

Mathematical Induction

EMORY UNIVERSITY SERIES

Trevor Evans, Henry Sharp, Jr., and Bevan K. Youse

PRENTICE-HALL INTERNATIONAL, INC., *London*
PRENTICE-HALL OF AUSTRALIA, LTD., *Sydney*
PRENTICE-HALL OF CANADA, LTD., *Toronto*
PRENTICE-HALL FRANCE, S.A.R.L., *Paris*
PRENTICE-HALL OF INDIA (PRIVATE) LTD., *New Delhi*
PRENTICE-HALL OF JAPAN, INC., *Tokyo*
PRENTICE-HALL DE MEXICO, S.A., *Mexico City*

MATHEMATICAL INDUCTION

Bevan K. Youse

Assistant Professor of Mathematics
Emory University

PRENTICE-HALL, INC., Englewood Cliffs, N. J.

Preface

This monograph is the first in a projected series of studies prepared under the general direction of members of the Mathematics Department at Emory University. Each study is a detailed examination of a topic of special interest in elementary mathematics. A primary goal of the authors is to develop the selected topics in the language and spirit of modern mathematics. For this reason it is hoped that these studies may be useful not only as texts in courses for high school teachers but also as supplementary material for students in advanced courses in college. In selection of topics, as well as in their treatment, the authors have been guided by the experience gained through many years of work with high school teachers. Much of this work has been sponsored by the National Science Foundation.

The Principle of Mathematical Induction provides one of the most powerful methods of proof available to the mathematician. This technique of proof is also important in elementary mathematics. This monograph was written to illustrate the many varied applications of the Principle of Mathematical Induction in algebra, geometry, and trigonometry.

Chapter 1 includes the necessary introductory material. In Chapter 2, various versions of the principle of mathematical induction are discussed with examples of the role of mathematical induction as a method of proof. Inductive definitions and sigma notation are introduced in Chapter 3, and a proof of the binomial theorem is given. In Chapter 4, a number of well-known theorems from elementary mathematics are proved by mathematical induction. Chapter 5 consists of a list of a variety of theorems from elementary mathematics, all of which may be proved by mathematical induction.

Bevan K. Youse

Table of Contents

INTRODUCTION

Chapter One

1.1 Sets

A *set* is a collection of objects; the objects are called *elements*, or *members*, of the set. We speak of the set of positive integers, the set of books in the school library, the set of prime numbers, etc. If E represents the set of even integers, then 2 is an element of E; however, 5 is not an element of the set E.

If x is an element in a given set S, this membership of x in S is denoted by $x \in S$ (read "x is an element of S," "x is in S," or "x belongs to S"). If t is an element not in the set S, we write $t \notin S$ (read "t is not an element of S" or "t is not in S"). Thus, if E denotes the set of even integers, $4 \in E$ and $7 \notin E$.

Two different methods of describing a set are (1) listing names of the elements in the set and (2) giving characterizing properties and requiring that the elements of the set have these properties. For example, the set with 1, 2, 3, 4, 6, and 12 as its elements, denoted by $\{1, 2, 3, 4, 6, 12\}$, could also be described as the set that has as its elements the positive integral factors of 12. When we define a set by the second method, we often use the symbolism $\{x \mid x$ is a positive integral factor of 12$\}$ (read "the set of all x such that x is a positive integral factor of 12"). More generally, $\{x \mid$ statement about $x\}$ represents the set of all x such that the statement about x is true.

It is convenient to admit the existence of a set with no elements; this set is called the *empty* or *null set*, and it is usually denoted by ϕ. For example, if $T = \{x \mid x$ is a real number and $x^2 < 0\}$, then since the square of any real number is non-negative we have that T is the empty set.

Two sets are *equal* if and only if they contain exactly the same elements. For example, if $A = \{2, 3, 6\}$ and $B = \{3, 2, 6\}$, the sets A and B are equal since they contain the same elements. We denote equality between sets A and B by $A = B$. If S and T are two sets that do not contain exactly the same elements, then we say that the sets are unequal and denote this by $S \neq T$.

EXAMPLES

1. If $W = \{1, 2, 3\}$, then $1 \in W$, $2 \in W$, and $3 \in W$. However, $7 \notin W$, $\frac{1}{2} \notin W$, $\sqrt{5} \notin W$, etc.
2. If $V = \{x \mid x$ is an integer and $x^2 - 5x - 6 = 0\}$, then V is also given by $V = \{-1, 6\}$.
3. If $S = \{t \mid t$ is an integer greater than 10$\}$, then S contains such elements as 11, 12, 13, 14, and 15. A complete listing of all the elements in S is not possible, since the set contains an infinite number of elements; however, it is standard mathematical notation to denote this set by $\{11, 12, 13, 14, \cdots\}$.
4. If $T = \{2, 3, 5, 7\}$ and if $P = \{y \mid y$ is a positive prime factor of 210$\}$, then T and P contain the same elements; thus, $T = P$.
5. If $S = \{\frac{2}{3}, \frac{1}{2}\}$ and $T = \{\frac{2}{3}, \frac{3}{4}\}$, then $S \neq T$.

Let E denote the set of even integers and I denote the set of all integers. Since every element in E is also an element in I, we say that E is a *subset* of I. A set S is said to be a subset of a set T, denoted by $S \subseteq T$, if and only if every element in S is an element in T. Symbolically, $S \subseteq T$ if and only if $x \in S$ implies $x \in T$. It should be noted that by the definitions of equality and subset $A = B$ if and only if $A \subseteq B$ and $B \subseteq A$.

As a consequence of the definition of subset, we have $S \subseteq S$ for any set S. Furthermore, since the empty set ϕ has no elements, every element in ϕ is in any given set S; hence, $\phi \subseteq S$. In other words, by the definition of subset, every set is a subset of itself, and the empty set is a subset of any set.

EXAMPLES

1. Let $S = \{1, 2, 3\}$. The subsets of S are $\{1\}$, $\{2\}$, $\{3\}$, $\{1, 2\}$, $\{1, 3\}$, $\{2, 3\}$, $\{1, 2, 3\}$, and ϕ.
2. Let $T = \{x \mid x^2 = 1$ where x is a real number$\}$. Thus, $T = \{1, -1\}$, and the subsets of T are $\{1\}$, $\{-1\}$, $\{1, -1\}$, and ϕ.

1.2 Functions and Sequences

We often consider sets whose elements are ordered pairs of numbers. An ordered pair is denoted by (x, y) where x is called the *first coordinate* and y is called the *second coordinate*. The ordered pair (x, y) is defined to be *equal* to the ordered pair (u, v) if and only if $x = u$ and $y = v$.

We speak of the set S of ordered pairs of real numbers which satisfy the equation $2x + y = 7$. Since $2(3) + 1 = 7$, the ordered pair $(3, 1)$ is an element in S. Symbolically, if $S = \{(x, y) \mid x$ and y are real numbers and $2x + y = 7\}$, then $(3, 1) \in S$.

A *function* F is a set of ordered pairs such that no two pairs have the same first coordinate. The set of all first coordinates is called the *domain* of F, and the set of all second coordinates is called the *range* of F. Since ordered pairs of real numbers, such as $(3, 4)$, can be plotted in the coordinate plane, a function F, whose domain and range are subsets of the set of real numbers, can be interpreted geometrically by considering the collection of all points in the plane with coordinates (x, y) such that $(x, y) \in F$. This subset of the set of points in the coordinate plane is called the *graph* of F.

Let $F = \{(x, y) \mid 2x + y = 7$, where x and y are real numbers$\}$.

If $(a, b) \in F$, then $2a + b = 7$ and $b = 7 - 2a$; similarly, if $(a, c) \in F$, then $c = 7 - 2a$. Thus, $b = c$, and we conclude that F is a set of ordered pairs of real numbers such that no two distinct pairs have the same first coordinate. Therefore, F is a function. The graph of F is a straight line. (See Figure 1-1.)

Let F be any function. If D denotes the domain of F, and R denotes its range, then F can be considered to provide a rule, or correspondence, that associates with each element x in D a unique element y in R. The unique element $y \in R$ associated with $x \in D$ is often denoted by $F(x)$ (read "F of x," or "the value of F at x"). The element $F(x)$ in R corresponding to x in D is often called the image of x *under* F. If $F = \{(x, y) \mid 2x + y = 7\}$, then $F(2) = 3$, $F(3) = 1$, and $F(\sqrt{3}) = 7 - 2\sqrt{3}$.

To simplify the definition of some special types of functions, we often write, for example, "let F be a function defined by $F(x) = \sqrt{x - 1}$. If we agree that the domain of F is the set of all real numbers such that $F(x)$ is a real number, then F is completely determined. The domain is $\{x \mid x \text{ is real}, x \geq 1\}$, and the range is $\{y \mid y \text{ is real}, y \geq 0\}$. The number 2 is an element in the domain, and $F(2) = \sqrt{2 - 1} = 1$; hence, $(2, 1) \in F$. (See Figure 1-2.)

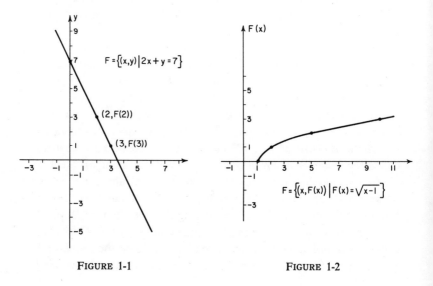

FIGURE 1-1   FIGURE 1-2

EXAMPLES

1. If $M = \{(1, 3), (-4, \frac{1}{2}), (0, \sqrt{3}\,)\}$, then M is a function. The domain D and the range R are given by $D = \{1, -4, 0\}$ and $R = \{3, \frac{1}{2}, \sqrt{3}\,\}$.
2. If $T = \{(1, 3), (-7, 4), (1, 6)\}$, then T is not a function, since two second coordinates, namely 3 and 6, are paired with 1.
3. If $F = \{(2, 3), (-11, \frac{1}{2}), (0, 3)\}$, then F is a function where $F(2) = 3$, $F(-11) = \frac{1}{2}$, and $F(0) = 3$.
4. If $F = \{(x, y) \mid x$ is a real number and $y = x^2\}$, then F is a function whose range is the set of non-negative real numbers. We have $F(0) = 0$, $F(-\frac{1}{2}) = \frac{1}{4}$, $F(\frac{1}{2}) = \frac{1}{4}$, $F(3) = 9$, etc.
5. If $G = \{(x, G(x)) \mid x$ is a real number and $G(x) = \sqrt{x^2 + 4}\}$, then G is a function where $G(0) = 2$, $G(1) = \sqrt{5}$, $G(-\sqrt{3}) = \sqrt{7}$, etc. The range of G is defined by $R = \{t \mid t$ is real, $t \geq 2\}$.

A *sequence* is a special type of function; it is a function whose domain is the set N of *positive integers*. A sequence is called a real sequence if its range is a subset of the set of real numbers. The value of the sequence S at n is usually denoted by S_n instead of $S(n)$; furthermore, S_n is called the nth term of the sequence. A sequence S is usually denoted by $\{S_n\}$ rather than by $\{(n, S_n)\}$.

EXAMPLES

1. If $S = \{(n, 1/n) \mid n$ is a positive integer$\}$, then S is a sequence. The nth term S_n is given by $S_n = 1/n$. Other notations for this sequence are $\{1/n\}$ and "$1, \frac{1}{2}, \frac{1}{3}, \frac{1}{4}, \frac{1}{5}, \cdots$."
2. If $S_n = 1$ when n is an even positive integer and $S_n = -1$ when n is an odd positive integer, then $\{S_n\}$ is a sequence that is also given by $\{(n, (-1)^n)\}$; that is, $-1, 1, -1, 1, -1, \cdots$, is the sequence of terms.
3. In the sequence defined by $S_n = n^2$ we have $S_1 = 1$, $S_2 = 4$, $S_3 = 9$, $S_4 = 16$, etc.
4. The sequence of even positive integers is defined by $S_n = 2n$. Note that $S_1 = 2$, $S_2 = 4$, $S_3 = 6$, $S_4 = 8$, etc.
5. The sequence of odd positive integers is defined by $S_n = 2n-1$. Note that $S_1 = 1$, $S_2 = 3$, $S_3 = 7$, $S_4 = 9$, etc.

PRINCIPLES OF MATHEMATICAL INDUCTION

Chapter Two

2.1 Introduction

We are often concerned in mathematics with such expressions as the following:

$$(1) \quad x + 3 = 2x + 1$$
$$(2) \quad 5x + 8 = 3x + 12$$
$$(3) \quad x^2 - 4 = (x - 2)(x + 2).$$

These are called *open sentences*; we cannot assert that an open sentence is either true or false. However, if we make some assertion as to what the symbol x (variable) represents, they become statements, or propositions, that are either true or false. For example, the statement "for every real number x, $x + 3 = 2x + 1$" is a false statement, since if, say, $x = 1$, then $2x + 1 = 3$ and $x + 3 = 4$. However, the statement "there exists at least one real number x such that $x + 3 = 2x + 1$" is a true statement, since if $x = 2$, then $x + 3 = 5$ and $2x + 1 = 5$.

Let us consider the sequence of odd positive integers: 1, 3, 5, 7, 9, 11, $\cdots$. If we define a new sequence $\{S_n\}$ by letting $S_1 = 1$ and by letting S_n for $n > 1$ be the sum of the first n odd integers, then we could determine the first few terms of this sequence by simple computation.

$$
\begin{aligned}
S_1 &= 1 & &= 1 \\
S_2 &= 1 + 3 & &= 4 \\
S_3 &= 1 + 3 + 5 & &= 9 \\
S_4 &= 1 + 3 + 5 + 7 + 9 & &= 16 \\
S_5 &= 1 + 3 + 5 + 7 + 9 + 11 & &= 25 \\
S_6 &= 1 + 3 + 5 + 7 + 9 + 11 + 13 &&= 36
\end{aligned}
$$

We notice that $S_1 = 1^2$, $S_2 = 2^2$, $S_3 = 3^2$, $S_4 = 4^2$, $S_5 = 5^2$, and $S_6 = 6^2$. These results certainly suggest the following conjecture: For every positive integer n, $S_n = n^2$. Before we discuss a method to prove that our guess is correct, let us consider other mathematical statements which involve the positive integers.

1. For every positive integer n greater than 2, the sum of the interior angles of a polygon with n sides is $(n - 2)180$ degrees.
2. For every positive integer n, 2 is a factor of $n^2 + n$.
3. For every positive integer n greater than 2, there are no integers x, y, and z such that $x^n + y^n = z^n$.
4. For every positive integer n, $x^{n+1} - 1 = (x - 1)(x^n + x^{n-1} + \cdots + x + 1)$.[†]
5. For every positive integer n, the square of the sum of the first n positive integers is equal to the sum of the first n cubes.
6. For every positive integer n, $n^2 - n + 41$ is a prime number.

Of the above statements, statement 6 is false since $(41^2 - 41 + 41) = 41^2$ is obviously not a prime number. It should be noted,

----

† This notation is meant to imply that $x^2 - 1 = (x - 1)(x + 1)$ for $n = 1$, $x^3 - 1 = (x - 1)(x^2 + x + 1)$ for $n = 2$, $x^4 - 1 = (x - 1)(x^3 + x^2 + x + 1)$ for $n = 3$, etc.

however, that $(n^2 - n + 41)$ is a prime number when n represents any of the first 40 positive integers. It is not known whether statement 3 is true or false; as a matter of fact, this is one of the famous unsolved problems in mathematics, known as Fermat's Last Theorem. However, statements 1, 2, 4, and 5 are true and can be proved by mathematical induction.

We often use the notation "$P(n)$" (read "P of n") to represent an open sentence, such as "2 is a factor of $n^2 + n$." If we say that $P(1)$ is true, we mean that the statement "2 is a factor of $1^2 + 1$" is a true statement. If we say that $P(n)$ is true for every positive integer, we mean that the statement "for every positive integer n, 2 is a factor of $n^2 + n$" is a true statement.

If we let "$P(n)$" denote the open sentence "$n^2 - n + 41$ is a prime number," then $P(1)$ would represent the true statement "$1^2 - 1 + 41$ is a prime number," and $P(41)$ would represent the false statement "$41^2 - 41 + 41$ is a prime number."

Let us return to the sequence $\{S_n\}$ associated with the sum of the first n odd numbers and our conjecture that $S_n = n^2$ for every positive integer n. If we let k be a positive integer for which $S_k = k^2$, then

$$1 + 3 + 5 + 7 + \cdots + (2k - 1) = k^2.$$

Hence, $1 + 3 + 5 + 7 + \cdots + (2k - 1) + (2k + 1)$, the sum of the first $k + 1$ odd numbers, is $k^2 + (2k + 1)$; that is, $(k + 1)^2$. Thus, if $S_n = n^2$ for $n = k$, we have proved that $S_n = n^2$ for $n = k + 1$. Since $S_6 = 6^2$, we can conclude that $S_7 = 7^2$; then, since $S_7 = 7^2$, we can conclude that $S_8 = 8^2$, etc.

We might *assume* that the reasoning used in the preceding paragraph indicates a general logical procedure for proving statements concerning the set of positive integers; that is, we could take what is called the First Principle of Induction (stated in the next section) as an axiom. However, we shall state the First Principle of Induction as a theorem; its proof will be based on the assumption that *every (nonempty) set of positive integers contains a smallest positive integer*. This is an *axiom* (assumption) for the positive integers and is usually called the *Well-ordering Axiom*. The reason for the approach of assuming the Well-ordering property and proving the

First Principle of Induction as a theorem is pedagogical. It can be proved that the Well-ordering property and the First Principle of Induction are equivalent statements; that is, one implies the other.

2.2 The First Principle of Induction

As an illustration of how the Well-ordering Axiom may be used to prove a statement about the positive integers, we now prove the following:

STATEMENT: For every positive integer n, 2 is a factor of $n^2 + n$.[†]

Proof: Let $P(n)$ denote the open sentence "2 is a factor of $n^2 + n$" and let $S = \{x \mid x$ is a positive integer and $P(x)$ is false$\}$; thus, if $x \in S$, then 2 is not a factor of $x^2 + x$. (Our approach is to show that the assumption that S is not the empty set leads to a contradiction.)

If S is not empty, we know by the Well-ordering Axiom that there is a smallest integer t in S. Hence, t is the smallest integer such that 2 is *not* a factor of $t^2 + t$. Since $1^2 + 1 = 2$ has 2 as a factor, t is greater than 1. Furthermore, we know that $(t - 1)^2 + (t - 1)$ has 2 as a factor, since $t - 1 < t$.

Since $2t$ has 2 as a factor, the sum $[(t - 1)^2 + (t - 1)] + 2t$ has 2 as a factor. But

$$(t - 1)^2 + (t - 1) + 2t = t^2 - 2t + 1 + t - 1 + 2t = t^2 + t.$$

Therefore, $t^2 + t$ has 2 as a factor which contradicts the preceding statement that 2 is not a factor of $t^2 + t$.

Thus, we conclude that there is no smallest integer t such that 2 is not a factor of $t^2 + t$; in other words, the set S must be empty, and 2 is a factor of $n^2 + n$ for every positive integer n.

The method of proof in this example can be used to prove the First Principle of Mathematical Induction.

[†] This is often stated as "2 is a factor of $n^2 + n$"; in this case, "for every positive integer n" is implied. However, we shall avoid this practice.

THEOREM 2.1   *First Principle of Induction.* Let $P(n)$ be an open sentence about positive integers, and assume the following:

(a) $P(1)$ is a true statement.

(b) For any integer $k \geq 1$, if $P(k)$ is true then $P(k + 1)$ is true.

Conclusion: $P(n)$ is true for every positive integer.

Proof: Let $S = \{x \mid x$ is a positive integer and $P(x)$ is a false statement$\}$. (We shall assume that S is not empty, and, as in the example, this will lead to a contradiction.)

If S is not empty, we know by the Well-ordering Axiom that there is a smallest integer t in S; that is, t *is the least positive integer such that* $P(t)$ *is false.* By hypothesis (a), $P(1)$ is true; thus, $t \neq 1$. Furthermore, $P(t - 1)$ is true since $t - 1 < t$.

By hypothesis (b), since $P(t - 1)$ is true, $P((t - 1) + 1)$ is true; that is, $P(t)$ is true. This contradicts the statement that $P(t)$ is false. Thus, the set S must be empty, and we conclude that $P(n)$ is true for every positive integer.

This theorem gives us a method that can often be used to prove such statements as "for every positive integer n, $P(n)$" are true without the necessity of employing the Well-ordering Axiom directly, as in our example. According to the theorem, $P(n)$ is true for every positive integer provided (i) we can show that $P(1)$ is true *and* (ii) we can show that $P(k + 1)$ is true on the assumption that $P(k)$ is true.

Let us illustrate this procedure by the following examples:

EXAMPLES

1. If a segment AB of unit length is given prove that, a line segment of length $\sqrt{n}$ can be constructed by straightedge and compass for every positive integer n.

    Proof: Let "$P(n)$" denote the open sentence "a segment of length $\sqrt{n}$ is constructable by straightedge and compass." Since $\sqrt{1} = 1$, and since a segment of unit length is given, $P(1)$ is clearly true.

    Now, *assume* that we can construct a segment of length $\sqrt{k}$

by straightedge and compass for some positive integer k. On the unit line segment AB construct at B, say, a line segment BC perpendicular to AB and of length $\sqrt{k}$. (We have assumed that a line segment of length $\sqrt{k}$ can be constructed, and we know that a line can be constructed perpendicular to a given line at a given point by straightedge and compass.) By the Pythagorean Theorem we conclude that the line segment AC has length $\sqrt{k+1}$. (See Figure 2-1.)

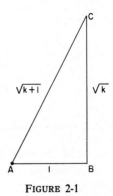

FIGURE 2-1

We have shown that $P(1)$ is true and that $P(k+1)$ is true if $P(k)$ is true. According to the First Principle of Induction, this is all that is required in order to conclude that $P(n)$ is true for every positive integer n; that is, a line segment of length $\sqrt{n}$ can be constructed with straightedge and compass for every positive integer n.

2. Let $P(n)$ denote the following open sentence:
$$x^{n+1} - 1 = (x - 1)(x^n + x^{n-1} + x^{n-2} + \cdots + x + 1).$$
Prove that $P(n)$ is true for every positive integer n.

Proof: Step 1. Since $x^2 - 1 = (x - 1)(x + 1)$, the statement $P(1)$ is true.

Step 2. Assume that $P(k)$ is true; that is, assume that
$$x^{k+1} - 1 = (x - 1)(x^k + x^{k-1} + x^{k-2} + \cdots + x + 1)$$
is a true statement. Now
$$\begin{aligned}
x^{k+2} - 1 &= x(x^{k+1}) - 1 \\
&= x(x^{k+1}) - x + x - 1 \\
&= x(x^{k+1} - 1) + (x - 1).
\end{aligned}$$
Thus, by the assumption that $P(k)$ is true, we have
$$\begin{aligned}
x^{k+2} - 1 &= (x)[(x - 1)(x^k + x^{k-1} + \cdots + x + 1)] + (x - 1) \\
&= (x - 1)(x^{k+1} + x^k + \cdots + x^2 + x) + (x - 1) \\
&= (x - 1)(x^{k+1} + x^k + \cdots + x^2 + x + 1);
\end{aligned}$$
hence,

$$x^{k+2} - 1 = (x - 1)(x^{k+1} + x^k + \cdots + x^2 + x + 1)$$

is a true statement. Therefore, we have proved that $P(k + 1)$ is true on the assumption that $P(k)$ is true. As a consequence of Theorem 2.1, Steps 1 and 2 prove that $P(n)$ is true for every positive integer.

2.3 Other Induction Principles

The theorem concerning mathematical induction most often found in elementary texts is the First Principle of Induction, but there are several variations of mathematical induction and each is quite useful. For example, we may be confronted with an open sentence $P(n)$ such that $P(1)$ is false, $P(2)$ is false, and $P(t)$ is false if t is an integer less than some integer a; however, it may be that $P(n)$ is true for every integer $n \geq a$.

The following example illustrates a statement of this type.

EXAMPLE

Let $P(n)$ be the following open sentence: $2^n < n!$ (where $n! = 1 \cdot 2 \cdot 3 \cdot 4 \cdots n$). If one substitutes 1, 2, or 3 for n, each of the resulting statements is false; for example, $2^3 > 3!$. However, these are the only positive integers for which the statement is false. We now prove that $P(n)$ is true for every positive integer greater than or equal to 4.

In order to prove this, let us consider the open sentence $Q(m)$ which is

$$2^{m+3} < (m + 3)!.$$

If m is any positive integer, then $m + 3 \geq 4$; hence, if $Q(m)$ is true for every positive integer, it will follow that $P(n)$ is true for every positive integer $n \geq 4$. We use the First Principle of Induction to prove that $Q(m)$ is true for every positive integer m. For $m = 1$, $2^{m+3} = 2^{1+3} = 2^4 = 16$, and $(m+3)! = (1+3)! = 4! = 24$; thus,

$$2^{1+3} < (1 + 3)!$$

is a true statement; that is, $Q(1)$ is true. Assume that $Q(m)$ is true for some positive integer k; that is, assume that

$$2^{k+3} < (k+3)!$$

is a true statement. Multiplying by 2 gives the true statement

$$2^{k+4} < 2(k+3)!\,.$$

Since $2 < k+4$ for any positive integer k,

$$2(k+3)! < (k+3)!(k+4) = (k+4)!;$$

hence,

$$2^{(k+1)+3} = 2^{k+4} < (k+4)! = [(k+1)+3]!,$$

and $Q(k+1)$ is true. By Theorem 2.1, $Q(m)$ is true for every positive integer; thus, $P(n)$ is true for every integer $n \geq 4$.

THEOREM 2.2   Let $P(t)$ be an open sentence about integers, and assume the following:
  (a) For some integer a, $P(a)$ is a true statement.
  (b) For any integer $k \geq a$, if $P(k)$ is true, then $P(k+1)$ is true.

Conclusion: $P(t)$ is true for every integer t greater than or equal to a.

Proof: Let $Q(m)$ be the open sentence $P(m-1+a)$. Now, if m is any positive integer, then $m-1+a \geq a$. Therefore, if we can prove that $Q(m)$ is true for every positive integer, then $P(t)$ is true for every integer $t \geq a$. Thus, we use the First Principle of Induction to show that $Q(m)$ is true for every positive integer. By the definition of $Q(m)$, $Q(1)$ is the statement

$$P(1-1+a) = P(a).$$

By hypothesis (a), $P(a)$ is true, and it follows that $Q(1)$ is true.

Assume that $Q(k)$ is true for some integer $k \geq 1$. Again, by definition of $Q(m)$, this means that

$$P(k-1+a)$$

is true.

By hypothesis (b), $P((k+1)-1+a)$ is true; that is,

$$P(k+a) = Q(k+1)$$

is true.

Therefore, by the First Principle of Induction, we conclude that $Q(m)$ is true for every positive integer and $P(t)$ is true for every positive integer $t \geq a$.[†]

Another theorem concerning mathematical induction (often called the Second Principle of Mathematical Induction) is the following:

THEOREM 2.3   *Second Principle.* Let $P(n)$ be an open sentence about positive integers and assume the following:
 (a) $P(1)$ is a true statement;
 (b) For any positive integer k, if $P(y)$ is true for every positive integer $y < k$, then $P(k)$ is true.
Conclusion: $P(n)$ is a true statement for every positive integer.

Proof: Let $S = \{x \,|\, x$ is a positive integer and $P(x)$ is false$\}$. If S is not empty, let t be the least integer in S;[‡] that is, t is the smallest positive integer such that $P(t)$ is false. Then, $P(y)$ is true for every positive integer $y < t$, and by hypothesis (b) we have that $P(t)$ is true. This contradiction proves that $P(n)$ is true for every positive integer.

EXAMPLE

The so-called Fibonacci sequence is defined as follows:
$$a_1 = 1, \quad a_2 = 2, \quad \text{and} \quad a_n = a_{n-1} + a_{n-2}$$
for all $n > 2$. (See Chapter Three for a detailed discussion of such definitions.) Now, using the Second Principle of Induction, we may prove that $a_n < (\frac{7}{4})^n$ for every positive integer n. For $n = 1$ and $n = 2$, it is clearly true that $a_n < (\frac{7}{4})^n$, since $1 = a_1 < (\frac{7}{4})^1 = \frac{7}{4}$ and $2 = a_2 < (\frac{7}{4})^2 = \frac{49}{16}$.
    Assume for an integer $k > 2$ that $P(y)$ is true for all $y < k$. Now, we wish to show that this assumption implies that $P(k)$ is true; that is, we wish to show this assumption implies $a_k < (\frac{7}{4})^k$. By assumption, $P(k-1)$ and $P(k-2)$ are true;

---

† Note that we do *not* assume that a is positive.
‡ Since $P(1)$ is true, $t > 1$.

that is,

$$a_{k-1} < (\tfrac{7}{4})^{k-1} \quad \text{and} \quad a_{k-2} < (\tfrac{7}{4})^{k-2}$$

are true statements. Therefore,

$$a_k = a_{k-1} + a_{k-2} < (\tfrac{7}{4})^{k-1} + (\tfrac{7}{4})^{k-2} = (\tfrac{7}{4})^{k-2}(\tfrac{7}{4} + 1)$$
$$= (\tfrac{7}{4})^{k-2}(\tfrac{11}{4}) < (\tfrac{7}{4})^{k-2}(\tfrac{7}{4})^2 = (\tfrac{7}{4})^k.$$

Thus, $a_k < (\tfrac{7}{4})^k$, and, by Theorem 2.3, $P(n)$ is true for every positive integer.

Our final theorem on mathematical induction gives another method for proving statements about positive integers. Although this theorem is not used often, it does give the reader some idea of the variety of induction proofs that can be employed to prove statements about the positive integers. We shall use it to prove an important inequality known as Jensen's Inequality. (See Chapter Four, Exercise 17.)

THEOREM 2.4 Let $P(n)$ be an open sentence about the positive integers and assume the following:

(a) $P(2^k)$ is true for every positive integer k.

(b) For any positive integer u, if $P(u)$ is true, then $P(u - 1)$ is true.

Conclusion: $P(n)$ is true for every positive integer.

Proof: Let $S = \{x \mid x \text{ is an integer and } P(x) \text{ is false}\}$. If S is nonempty, there exists a smallest integer t such that $P(t)$ is false. By hypothesis (a), $P(n)$ is true for every integral power of 2. Hence, there exists some positive integer v such that $2^v > t$. Let d be the difference $2^v - t$; that is, let $d = 2^v - t$.

Now, if $P(t + 1)$ is true, by hypothesis (b) we would have that $P(t)$ is true. This is a contradiction. If $P(t + 1)$ is false, by a similar argument we could conclude that $P(t + 2)$, $P(t + 3)$, $P(t + 4)$, $\cdots$, $P(t + d)$ are false. However, since $t + d = 2^v$, this would imply that $P(2^v)$ is false, a contradiction to hypothesis (a). Thus, $P(n)$ is true for every positive integer.[†]

† It should be noted that 2 has no special role in the proof of this theorem; in other words, 2^k could be replaced by 3^k, 4^k, etc. In fact, in hypothesis (a) we could replace 2^k by a_k where $\{a_k\}$ is any (unbounded) sequence of positive integers with the property that $a_k < a_{k+1}$.

APPLICATIONS

Chapter Three

3.1 Inductive Definitions

Most students are aware of the fact that mathematical definitions should be both precise and rigorous. Admittedly, this ideal is not always easy to attain, even in elementary mathematics. In high-school geometry, for example, some concepts—such as the polygon—turn out to be more difficult to define than appears from a cursory consideration.

Certain concepts depend for their precise definitions on what is called an *inductive definition*. Often, attempts are made to define these concepts without recourse to an inductive definition. This results, of course, in a lack of precision that sometimes prevents a thorough understanding of the concept to be defined.

To illustrate what is called an inductive definition, let us consider the definition of positive integral exponents. The idea is to give a meaning to the symbol a^n, where a is a real number, for every positive integer n. With this in mind, we propose the following definition of a^n:

DEFINITION 3.1 For any real number a, we define

(1) $a^1 = a$;

(2) $a^{k+1} = (a^k) \cdot a$, where k is a positive integer.

This definition permits us to prove that a^n is defined for every positive integer n. If a^n is not defined for some positive integer n, then the set S of positive integers for which a^n is not defined is nonempty. Let t be the least positive integer in S. By (1), we have that $t \neq 1$, and, thus, $(t - 1)$ is a positive integer. Furthermore, a^{t-1} is defined, since $t - 1 < t$. By (2), $a^{(t-1)+1} = (a^{t-1}) \cdot a$; that is, $a^t = (a^{t-1}) \cdot a$. Hence, since a^t is defined, we have a contradiction. We conclude that S is empty and a^n is defined for every positive integer.

As a consequence of Definition 3.1 (and the associative law of multiplication),

$$a^1 = a,$$
$$a^2 = a^{1+1} = (a^1) \cdot a = a \cdot a,$$
$$a^3 = a^{2+1} = (a^2) \cdot a = (a \cdot a) \cdot a = a \cdot a \cdot a,$$
$$a^4 = a^{3+1} = (a^3) \cdot a = (a \cdot a \cdot a) \cdot a = a \cdot a \cdot a \cdot a.$$

It should be clear from this example of an inductive definition that if a concept involving the positive integers is defined for 1 and is also defined for the integer $(k + 1)$ whenever it is defined for k, then it is defined for every positive integer.

3.2 Sigma Notation and Applications

Let $\{a_n\}$ be the sequence defined by $a_n = 2n$; that is, $a_1 = 2$, $a_2 = 4$, $a_3 = 6$, $a_4 = 8$, etc. If we wanted to express the sum of the first eight terms of this sequence of even integers, we could write

$$2 + 4 + 6 + 8 + 10 + 12 + 14 + 16;$$

to express the sum of the first one-hundred terms we could write

$$2 + 4 + 6 + 8 + \cdots + 198 + 200.$$

However, there is a very convenient notation called the *sigma no-*

tation which can be used to avoid such "addition strings." The following is an inductive definition of the sigma notation.

DEFINITION 3.2   For any sequence of numbers $\{a_n\}$,

(1) $\displaystyle\sum_{u=1}^{1} a_u = a_1$;

(2) $\displaystyle\sum_{u=1}^{k+1} a_u = \left(\sum_{u=1}^{k} a_u\right) + a_{k+1}$, where k is a positive integer.

Since $\displaystyle\sum_{u=1}^{n} a_u$ is defined for the positive integer 1, and since it is also defined for $k+1$ when it is defined for the positive integer k, $\displaystyle\sum_{u=1}^{k} a_u$ is defined for every positive integer n.

As a consequence of Definition 3.2 (and the associative law of addition),

$$\sum_{u=1}^{1} a_u = a_1,$$

$$\sum_{u=1}^{2} a_u = \left(\sum_{u=1}^{1} a_u\right) + a_2 = a_1 + a_2,$$

$$\sum_{u=1}^{3} a_u = \left(\sum_{u=1}^{2} a_u\right) + a_3 = (a_1 + a_2) + a_3 = a_1 + a_2 + a_3,$$

$$\sum_{u=1}^{4} a_u = \left(\sum_{u=1}^{3} a_u\right) + a_4 = (a_1 + a_2 + a_3) + a_4$$

$$= a_1 + a_2 + a_3 + a_4.$$

We see that

$$\sum_{u=1}^{8} (2u) = 2 + 4 + 6 + 8 + 10 + 12 + 14 + 16$$

and that the sum of the first one-hundred even positive integers can be denoted conveniently by $\displaystyle\sum_{u=1}^{100} (2u)$.

Let us prove some of the basic properties associated with the sigma notation; the method of proof will be mathematical induction.

THEOREM 3.1   For every positive integer n,

$$\sum_{u=1}^{n}(a_u + b_u) = \sum_{u=1}^{n}a_u + \sum_{u=1}^{n}b_u.$$

Proof: (1) Since

$$\sum_{u=1}^{1}a_u = a_1, \quad \sum_{u=1}^{1}b_u = b_1,$$

and

$$\sum_{u=1}^{1}(a_u + b_u) = a_1 + b_1,$$

we have

$$\sum_{u=1}^{1}(a_u + b_u) = \sum_{u=1}^{1}a_u + \sum_{u=1}^{1}b_u.$$

Thus, the statement is true for $n = 1$.

(2) For any integer $k \geq 1$, assume that

$$\sum_{u=1}^{k}(a_u + b_u) = \sum_{u=1}^{k}a_u + \sum_{u=1}^{k}b_u$$

is a true statement. Now,

$$\sum_{u=1}^{k+1}(a_u + b_u) = \sum_{u=1}^{k}(a_u + b_u) + (a_{k+1} + b_{k+1}) \qquad \text{(Definition 3.2)}$$

$$= \left(\sum_{u=1}^{k}a_u + \sum_{u=1}^{k}b_u\right) + (a_{k+1} + b_{k+1}) \qquad \text{(Assumption)}$$

$$= \left(\sum_{u=1}^{k}a_u\right) + a_{k+1} + \left(\sum_{u=1}^{k}b_u\right) + b_{k+1}$$

$$= \sum_{u=1}^{k+1}a_u + \sum_{u=1}^{k+1}b_u. \qquad \text{(Definition 3.2)}$$

Thus, on the assumption that the statement is true for k we have proved that it is true for the integer $(k + 1)$. By the First Principle of Induction, we conclude that the theorem is true.

THEOREM 3.2 For every positive integer n, $\sum_{u=1}^{n}ca_u = c\sum_{u=1}^{n}a_u$ where c is a real number.[†]

[†] This is a statement of what is often called the Generalized Distributive Law.

Proof: (1)   Since

$$\sum_{u=1}^{1} ca_u = ca_1 = c \sum_{u=1}^{1} a_u,$$

the statement is true for $n = 1$.

(2)   For any integer $k \geq 1$, assume that

$$\sum_{u=1}^{k} ca_u = c \sum_{u=1}^{k} a_u$$

is a true statement. Thus,

$$\sum_{u=1}^{k+1} ca_u = \left(\sum_{u=1}^{k} ca_u \right) + ca_{k+1} \qquad \text{(Definition 3.2)}$$

$$= c \sum_{u=1}^{k} a_u + ca_{k+1} \qquad \text{(Assumption)}$$

$$= c \left(\sum_{u=1}^{k} a_u + a_{k+1} \right) \qquad \text{(Distributive law)}$$

$$= c \sum_{u=1}^{k+1} a_u \qquad \text{(Definition 3.2)}$$

As a consequence of the First Principle of Induction, we conclude that the theorem is true.

THEOREM 3.3   For every positive integer n,

$$\sum_{u=1}^{n} (a_{u+1} - a_u) = a_{n+1} - a_1.$$

(This is often called the *telescoping property* for the sigma notation.)

Proof: (1)   Since by Definition 3.2

$$\sum_{u=1}^{1} (a_{u+1} - a_u) = a_2 - a_1$$

and

$$a_{n+1} - a_1 = a_2 - a_1 \quad \text{for} \quad n = 1,$$

we have

$$\sum_{u=1}^{1} (a_{u+1} - a_u) = a_2 - a_1,$$

and the statement is true for $n = 1$.

(2)   For any integer $k \geq 1$, assume that

$$\sum_{u=1}^{k} (a_{u+1} - a_u) = a_{k+1} - a_1$$

is a true statement. Then,

$$\sum_{u=1}^{k+1} (a_{u+1} - a_u) = \left(\sum_{u=1}^{k} (a_{u+1} - a_u) \right) + (a_{k+1} - a_k) \quad \text{(Definition 3.2)}$$

$$= (a_{k+1} - a_1) + (a_{k+2} - a_{k+1}) \qquad \text{(Assumption)}$$

$$= a_{k+2} - a_1$$

We have shown that the statement is true for $n = 1$ and that if the statement is true for k, it is also true for $k + 1$. Consequently, the statement is true for every positive integer.

In the sigma notation $\sum_{u=1}^{10} u^2$, the number 10 is called the upper value of summation, and 1 is called the lower value. We have defined the sigma notation for any upper value of summation when the lower value is 1. It is sometimes convenient to change the *lower value* of summation on the sigma notation. For example, we may wish to consider

$$\sum_{u=4}^{7} u^2 \quad \text{or} \quad \sum_{u=0}^{4} (u + 2)^3.$$

We define $\sum_{u=0}^{n} a_u$ by the following:

$$\sum_{u=0}^{n} a_u = a_0 + \sum_{u=1}^{n} a_u.$$

Furthermore, if t is an integer greater than 1 and less than n, we define $\sum_{u=t}^{n} a_u$ by the following:

$$\sum_{u=t}^{n} a_u = \sum_{u=1}^{n} a_u - \sum_{u=1}^{t-1} a_u.$$

Thus,

(1) $\sum_{u=4}^{7} u^2 = \sum_{u=1}^{7} u^2 - \sum_{u=1}^{3} u^2 = 4^2 + 5^2 + 6^2 + 7^2;$

(2) $\sum_{u=0}^{4} (u + 2)^3 = (0 + 2)^3 + \sum_{u=1}^{4} (u + 2)^3$

$$= 2^3 + 3^3 + 4^3 + 5^3 + 6^3;$$

(3) $\displaystyle\sum_{u=1}^{10}(2u-1)=\sum_{u=0}^{9}(2u+1)=\sum_{u=4}^{13}(2u-7);$

(4) $\displaystyle\sum_{u=0}^{n}a_u=\sum_{u=1}^{n+1}a_{u-1}.$

Before concluding this section, let us consider an example involving the sigma notation and mathematical induction. In this example we shall exhibit a proof that the sum of the first n positive integers is $n(n+1)/2$.

EXAMPLE

For every positive integer n,

$$\sum_{u=1}^{n}u=\frac{n(n+1)}{2}.$$

Proof: (1)   Since

$$\sum_{u=1}^{1}u=1=\frac{1(1+1)}{2},$$

the statement is true for the positive integer 1.

(2)   Assume that

$$\sum_{u=1}^{k}u=\frac{k(k+1)}{2}$$

is a true statement. We want to prove that as a consequence of this assumption

$$\sum_{u=1}^{k+1}u=\frac{(k+1)(k+2)}{2}$$

is a true statement. Now,

$$\sum_{u=1}^{k+1}u=\sum_{u=1}^{k}u+(k+1) \qquad \text{(Definition 3.2)}$$

$$=\frac{k(k+1)}{2}+(k+1) \qquad \text{(Assumption)}$$

$$=\frac{k(k+1)+2(k+1)}{2}$$

$$=\frac{(k+1)(k+2)}{2}.$$

Since $n(n + 1)/2 = (k + 1)(k + 2)/2$ when $n = k + 1$, the statement is true for the integer $k + 1$. We conclude that

$$\sum_{u=1}^{n} u = \frac{n(n + 1)}{2}$$

for every positive integer n.

With a little resourcefulness one can *derive* the formula for the sum of the first n positive integers. Since

$$(u + 1)^2 - u^2 = 2u + 1$$

is an algebraic identity, we have

$$(u + 1)^2 - u^2 = 2u + 1$$

for every positive integer u. Hence,

$$\sum_{u=1}^{n} [(u + 1)^2 - u^2] = \sum_{u=1}^{n} (2u + 1).$$

By Theorem 3.3,

$$\sum_{u=1}^{n} [(u + 1)^2 - u^2] = (n + 1)^2 - 1^2 = n^2 + 2n;$$

furthermore,

$$\sum_{u=1}^{n} (2u + 1) = \sum_{u=1}^{n} 2u + \sum_{u=1}^{n} 1 \qquad \text{(Theorem 3.1)}$$

$$= 2\left(\sum_{u=1}^{n} u\right) + n. \qquad \text{(Theorem 3.2)\dag}$$

Consequently,

$$2\left(\sum_{u=1}^{n} u\right) + n = n^2 + 2n$$

$$2\left(\sum_{u=1}^{n} u\right) = n^2 + n$$

$$\sum_{u=1}^{n} u = \frac{n(n + 1)}{2}.$$

It should be noted that the second proof that the sum of the first n positive integers is $n(n + 1)/2$ makes use of math-

---

\dag If $a_u = 1$, then $\sum_{u=1}^{n} a_u$ or $\sum_{u=1}^{n} 1$ represents the sum of n ones.

ematical induction, since the properties of the sigma notation
were proved by mathematical induction.

3.3 Binomial Theorem

The notation $n!$ (read "n factorial") is defined inductively for
the positive integers in the following way:

DEFINITION 3.3

(1) $1! = 1$;
(2) $(k + 1)! = (k + 1)(k!)$.

Thus,

$$2! = (2)(1!) = 2 \times 1; \quad 3! = (3)(2!) = 3 \times 2 \times 1.$$

In general,

$$n! = n \times (n - 1) \times (n - 2) \times \cdots \times 2 \times 1.$$

Furthermore, it is convenient, as we shall see later, to define $0!$ as
1.

If k and i are integers such that $0 \leq i \leq k$, the *binomial coefficient* ${}_kC_i$ is defined by

$$_kC_i = \frac{k!}{i!(k - i)!}.^\dagger$$

EXAMPLES

1. $_4C_3 = \dfrac{4!}{(3!)(1!)} = \dfrac{4 \times 3 \times 2 \times 1}{3 \times 2 \times 1} = 4.$

2. $_7C_1 = \dfrac{7!}{(1!)(6!)} = \dfrac{7 \times 6 \times 5 \times 4 \times 3 \times 2 \times 1}{6 \times 5 \times 4 \times 3 \times 2 \times 1} = 7.$

3. $_8C_3 = \dfrac{8!}{(3!)(5!)} = \dfrac{8 \times 7 \times 6 \times 5 \times 4 \times 3 \times 2 \times 1}{(3 \times 2 \times 1)(5 \times 4 \times 3 \times 2 \times 1)}$

$$= \frac{8 \times 7 \times 6}{3 \times 2 \times 1} = 56.$$

---

† Other notations for $_kC_i$ are $\binom{k}{i}$, $\{k\}_i$, and C_i^k.

4. $\ _{12}C_9 = \dfrac{12!}{(9!)(3!)} = \dfrac{12 \times 11 \times 10}{3 \times 2 \times 1} = 220.$

For integers k and i, $_kC_i$ is the number of subsets with i elements of a given set containing k elements; thus, $_kC_i$ is often read "the number of k things taken i at a time."

Consider the sum $_5C_4 + \,_5C_3$. Since

$$_5C_4 = \frac{5!}{(4!)(1!)} = 5 \quad \text{and} \quad _5C_3 = \frac{5!}{(3!)(2!)} = 10,$$

we have $\qquad\qquad\qquad _5C_4 + \,_5C_3 = 15.$

Furthermore,

$$_6C_4 = \frac{6!}{(4!)(2!)} = \frac{6 \times 5}{2 \times 1} = 15.$$

Thus, $\qquad\qquad\qquad\qquad _5C_4 + \,_5C_3 = \,_6C_4.$

This illustrates an important property for the binomial coefficients which we now justify.

If $0 \leq i \leq k$, then

$$\begin{aligned}
_kC_i + \,_kC_{i-1} &= \frac{k!}{(i!)(k-i)!} + \frac{k!}{(i-1)!(k-i+1)!} \\
&= \frac{k!(k-i+1) + k!(i)}{(i!)(k-i+1)!} \\
&= \frac{k!(k+1) - k!(i) + k!(i)}{(i!)(k-i+1)!} \\
&= \frac{(k+1)!}{(i!)(k+1-i)} \\
&= \,_{k+1}C_i.
\end{aligned}$$

We shall use this property in the following proof of the Binomial Theorem.

THEOREM 3.4   For every positive integer n,

$$(x+y)^n = \sum_{u=0}^{n} {_nC_u} x^{n-u} y^u$$

where x and y are real numbers.

---

† A future monograph of this series will discuss combinations and related topics.

Proof: (1) $\displaystyle\sum_{u=0}^{1} {}_1C_u x^{1-u} y^u = {}_1C_0 x^1 y^0 + {}_1C_1 x^0 y^1$

$$= x + y$$

$$= (x + y)^1$$

(2)   Assume that the statement is true for the positive integer k; that is, assume that

$$(x + y)^k = \sum_{u=0}^{k} {}_kC_u x^{k-u} y^u$$

is a true statement. Thus,

$$(x + y)^{k+1} = (x + y)(x + y)^k$$

$$= x(x + y)^k + y(x + y)^k$$

$$= x \sum_{u=0}^{k} {}_kC_u x^{k-u} y^u + y \sum_{u=0}^{k} {}_kC_u x^{k-u} y^u$$

$$= \sum_{u=0}^{k} {}_kC_u x^{k-u+1} y^u + \sum_{u=0}^{k} {}_kC_u x^{k-u} y^{u+1}$$

$$= {}_kC_0 x^{k+1} y^0 + \sum_{u=1}^{k} {}_kC_u x^{k-u+1} y^u + \sum_{u=0}^{k-1} {}_kC_u x^{k-u} y^{u+1}$$
$$+ {}_kC_0 x^0 y^{k+1}$$

$$= x^{k+1} + \sum_{u=1}^{k} {}_kC_u x^{k-u+1} y^u + \sum_{u=1}^{k} {}_kC_{u-1} x^{k-u+1} y^u$$
$$+ y^{k+1}$$

$$= x^{k+1} + \sum_{u=1}^{k} ({}_kC_u + {}_kC_{u-1}) x^{k-u+1} y^u + y^{k+1}$$

$$= x^{k+1} + \sum_{u=1}^{k} {}_{k+1}C_u x^{k-u+1} y^u + y^{k+1}$$

$$= \sum_{u=0}^{k+1} {}_{k+1}C_u x^{k+1-u} y^u .$$

Thus, we have shown that the statement is true for $n = k + 1$ on the assumption that it is true for $n = k$. The theorem is proved.

STATEMENTS PROVED BY
MATHEMATICAL INDUCTION

Chapter Four

In this chapter we state a number of theorems and give a mathematical induction proof of each of them.

1. If $0 < x < 1$, then $0 < x^n < 1$ for every positive integer n.

Proof: (1) By hypothesis, $0 < x^1 < 1$.

(2) Assume that $0 < x^k < 1$ for some positive integer k. Since $x^k > 0$ and $x > 0$, we have $x^{k+1} > 0$; furthermore, since $x^k < 1$ and $x < 1$ and since x^k and x are both positive, we have $x^{k+1} < 1$. Thus

$$0 < x^{k+1} < 1.$$

Hence, we have proved that the proposition is true for $(k + 1)$ if it is true for the integer k. As a consequence of (1) and (2), the statement is proved.

2. For every positive integer n, $\cos n\pi = (-1)^n$.

Proof: (1) Since $\cos \pi = -1$, as a consequence of the definition of the cosine function, the statement is true for $n = 1$.

(2) Assume that $\cos k\pi = (-1)^k$ is a true statement. Using the fact that $\cos(x + y) = \cos x \cos y - \sin x \sin y$, we obtain

$$\cos(k + 1)\pi = \cos(k\pi + \pi)$$
$$= \cos k\pi \cos \pi - \sin k\pi \sin \pi$$
$$= (-1)^k(-1) - (\sin k\pi)(0)$$
$$= (-1)^{k+1}.$$

Since we proved that $\cos n\pi = (-1)^n$ is a true statement for the positive integer 1 and that it is true for $k + 1$ on the assumption that it is true for k, we conclude that the statement is true for every positive integer.

3. For every positive integer n,

$$\frac{n^5}{5} + \frac{n^3}{3} + \frac{7n}{15}$$

is an integer.

Proof: (1) For $n = 1$, we have

$$\frac{1^5}{5} + \frac{1^3}{3} + \frac{(7)(1)}{15} = 1;$$

thus, the statement is true for the integer 1.

(2) Assume that

$$\frac{k^5}{5} + \frac{k^3}{3} + \frac{7k}{15}$$

is an integer. Using this assumption we want to prove that

$$\frac{(k + 1)^5}{5} + \frac{(k + 1)^3}{3} + \frac{7(k + 1)}{15}$$

is an integer. Let us consider each term separately. Now,

$$\frac{(k + 1)^5}{5} = \frac{k^5 + 5k^4 + 10k^3 + 10k^2 + 5k + 1}{5}.$$

(A) $\quad \dfrac{(k+1)^5}{5} = \dfrac{k^5}{5} + \dfrac{1}{5} + (k^4 + 2k^3 + 2k^2 + k),$

$\quad\quad \dfrac{(k+1)^3}{3} = \dfrac{k^3 + 3k^2 + 3k + 1}{3}.$

(B) $\quad \dfrac{(k+1)^3}{3} = \dfrac{k^3}{3} + \dfrac{1}{3} + (k^2 + k).$

(C) $\quad \dfrac{7(k+1)}{15} = \dfrac{7k}{15} + \dfrac{7}{15}.$

Adding equalities (A), (B), and (C), we get

$$\dfrac{(k+1)^5}{5} + \dfrac{(k+1)^3}{3} + \dfrac{7(k+1)}{15}$$

$$= \dfrac{k^5}{5} + \dfrac{k^3}{3} + \dfrac{7k}{15} + (k^4 + 2k^3 + 3k^2 + 2k + 1).$$

Since k is an integer, $(k^4 + 2k^3 + 3k^2 + 2k + 1)$ is an integer; furthermore,

$$\dfrac{k^5}{5} + \dfrac{k^3}{3} + \dfrac{7k}{15}$$

is an integer by assumption. Consequently,

$$\dfrac{(k+1)^5}{5} + \dfrac{(k+1)^3}{3} + \dfrac{7(k+1)}{15}$$

is an integer.

From (1) and (2) we conclude that

$$\dfrac{n^5}{5} + \dfrac{n^3}{3} + \dfrac{7n}{15}$$

is an integer for every positive integer n.

4. For every positive integer $n \geq 2$, the number of lines obtained by joining n distinct points in the plane, no three of which are collinear, is $n(n-1)/2$.

Proof: (1) Since $n(n-1)/2 = 1$ for $n = 2$ and since two distinct points determine one and only one line, the statement is true for $n = 2$.

(2)   Let $P_1, P_2, P_3, \cdots, P_k$ be k distinct points in the plane, no three of which are collinear. Assume that the k points determine $k(k-1)/2$ lines.

If another point P_{k+1} is added to the plane so that no three of the $k+1$ points are collinear, then P_{k+1} cannot be on any of the $k(k-1)/2$ lines determined by pairs of the given k points. Now, we want to prove that the $k+1$ points determine $(k+1)k/2$ lines.

Since P_{k+1} is not on any of the lines determined by the k points $P_1, P_2, P_3, \cdots, P_k$, we know that P_{k+1} and P_1, P_{k+1} and P_2, P_{k+1} and P_3, $\cdots$, P_{k+1} and P_k determine k additional distinct lines in the plane. In fact, these are the only additional lines obtained by joining all pairs of points. Hence, the number of lines determined by the $k+1$ points is $[k(k-1)/2] + k$. But

$$\frac{k(k-1)}{2} + k = \frac{k^2 - k + 2k}{2}$$

$$= \frac{k^2 + k}{2}$$

$$= \frac{(k+1)k}{2}.$$

Hence, as a consequence of parts (1) and (2) and Theorem 2.2, we conclude that the given statement is true.

5.   For every positive integer n, $6^{n+2} + 7^{2n+1}$ has 43 as a factor.

Proof: (1)   For $n = 1$,

$$6^3 + 7^3 = 216 + 343 = 559 = (13)(43).$$

Thus, the statement is true for the positive integer 1.

(2)   Assume that $6^{k+2} + 7^{2k+1}$ has 43 as a factor; that is, assume that

$$6^{k+2} + 7^{2k+1} = 43t$$

for some integer t. With this assumption we wish to prove that $6^{k+3} + 7^{2k+3}$ has 43 as a factor. Now,

$$6^{k+3} + 7^{2k+3} = 6^{k+3} + 6(7^{2k+1}) - 6(7^{2k+1}) + 7^{2k+3}$$

$$= 6(6^{k+2} + 7^{2k+1}) + 7^{2k+1}(7^2 - 6)$$
$$= 6(43t) + 7^{2k+1}(43)$$
$$= 43(6t + 7^{2k+1}).$$

Thus, $6^{k+3} + 7^{2k+3}$ has 43 as a factor.

From parts (1) and (2), we conclude that the statement is true.

6. For every positive integer n,

$$\sum_{u=1}^{n} \frac{1}{u(u+1)} = \frac{n}{n+1}.$$

Proof: (1) Since

$$\sum_{u=1}^{1} \frac{1}{u(u+1)} = \frac{1}{(1)(2)} = \frac{1}{2},$$

and since

$$\frac{n}{n+1} = \frac{1}{2}$$

for $n = 1$, we conclude that

$$\sum_{u=1}^{1} \frac{1}{u(u+1)} = \frac{1}{1+1},$$

and the statement is proved for the positive integer 1.

(2) Assume that

$$\sum_{u=1}^{k} \frac{1}{u(u+1)} = \frac{k}{k+1}$$

is a true statement. Thus,

$$\sum_{u=1}^{k+1} \frac{1}{u(u-1)} = \sum_{u=1}^{k} \frac{1}{u(u+1)} + \frac{1}{(k+1)(k+2)} \qquad \text{(Definition 3.2)}$$

$$= \frac{k}{k+1} + \frac{1}{(k+1)(k+2)} \qquad \text{(Assumption)}$$

$$= \frac{k^2 + 2k + 1}{(k+1)(k+2)} = \frac{(k+1)(k+1)}{(k+1)(k+2)}$$

$$= \frac{k+1}{k+2}.$$

Since we proved that the statement is true for $n = k + 1$ on the assumption that it is true for $n = k$, and since we proved the statement true for $n = 1$, we conclude that it is true for every positive integer.

[Note: This theorem can be proved by the telescoping property of the sigma notation if we notice that

$$\frac{1}{u(u + 1)} = \frac{1}{u} - \frac{1}{u + 1};$$

that is,

$$\sum_{u=1}^{n} \frac{1}{u(u + 1)} = \sum_{u=1}^{n} \left(\frac{1}{u} - \frac{1}{u + 1} \right) = \frac{1}{1} - \frac{1}{n + 1}$$

$$= \frac{n}{n + 1}]$$

7. For every positive integer n,

$$\sum_{u=1}^{n} ar^{u-1} = \frac{ar^n - a}{r - 1}$$

where a and r are real and $r \neq 1$.

Proof: (1) Since

$$\sum_{u=1}^{1} ar^{u-1} = ar^0 = a,$$

and since

$$\frac{ar^1 - a}{r - 1} = \frac{a(r - 1)}{(r - 1)} = a,$$

the statement is true for $n = 1$.

(2) Assume that

$$\sum_{u=1}^{k} ar^{u-1} = \frac{ar^k - a}{r - 1}.$$

Then,

$$\sum_{u=1}^{k+1} ar^{n-1} = \sum_{u=1}^{k} ar^{u-1} + ar^k$$

$$= \frac{ar^k - a}{r - 1} + ar^k$$

$$= \frac{ar^k - a + ar^{k+1} - ar^k}{r - 1}$$

$$= \frac{ar^{k+1} - a}{r - 1}.$$

By (1) and (2), we conclude that

$$\sum_{u=1}^{n} ar^{u-1} = \frac{ar^n - a}{r - 1}$$

for every positive integer n.

8. For every positive integer n,

$$\sum_{u=1}^{n} u^2 = \frac{n(n + 1)(2n + 1)}{6}.$$

Proof: (1) Since

$$\sum_{u=1}^{1} u^2 = 1,$$

and since $1(2)(3)/6 = 1$, the statement is true for $n = 1$.

(2) Assume that

$$\sum_{u=1}^{k} u^2 = \frac{k(k + 1)(2k + 1)}{6}$$

is a true statement. [On this assumption, we wish to prove that

$$\sum_{u=1}^{k+1} u^2 = \frac{(k + 1)(k + 2)(2k + 3)}{6}$$

is a true statement.]

Now,

$$\sum_{u=1}^{k+1} u^2 = \sum_{u=1}^{k} u^2 + (k + 1)^2 \qquad \text{(Definition 3.2)}$$

$$= \frac{k(k + 1)(2k + 3)}{6} + (k + 1)^2 \qquad \text{(Assumption)}$$

$$= (k + 1)\left[\frac{k(2k + 1) + 6(k + 1)}{6} \right]$$

$$= \frac{(k + 1)(2k^2 + 7k + 6)}{6}$$

$$= \frac{(k + 1)(k + 2)(2k + 3)}{6}.$$

Thus, by the First Principle of Induction, we conclude that the statement is true for every positive integer. [If we notice that $u^3 - (u - 1)^3 = 3u^2 - 3u + 1$, the formula for the sum of the square of the first n positive integers can be derived by using the properties of the sigma notation.]

9. For every positive integer n,

$$\sum_{u=1}^{n} u^3 = \frac{n^2(n + 1)^2}{4}.$$

Proof: (1) Let $P(n)$ denote the statement

$$\sum_{u=1}^{n} u^3 = \frac{n^2(n + 1)^2}{4}.$$

Since

$$\sum_{u=1}^{1} u^3 = 1$$

and since $[(1^2)(2)^2/4] = 1$, the statement $P(1)$ is true.

(2) Assume that $P(k)$ is true. Thus,

$$\sum_{u=1}^{k} u^3 = \frac{k^2(k + 1)^2}{4}$$

is a true statement. Now,

$$\sum_{u=1}^{k+1} u^3 = \sum_{u=1}^{k} u^3 + (k + 1)^3 \qquad \text{(Definition 3.2)}$$

$$= \frac{k^2(k + 1)^2}{4} + (k + 1)^3 \qquad \text{(Assumption)}$$

$$= (k + 1)^2 \left[\frac{k^2 + 4(k + 1)}{4} \right]$$

$$= \frac{(k + 1)^2(k + 2)^2}{4}$$

Thus, we conclude that $P(k + 1)$ is true if $P(k)$ is true.

Parts (1) and (2) prove that $P(n)$ is true for every positive integer n.

10. For every positive integer n,

$$x^n - y^n = (x - y)\left(\sum_{u=1}^{n} x^{n-u}y^{u-1}\right).$$

Proof: (1) For $n = 1$, we have

$$x^1 - y^1 = (x - y)\left(\sum_{u=1}^{1} x^{1-u}y^u\right) = (x - y)x^0y^0 = (x - y).$$

Thus, the statement is true for the positive integer 1.

(2) Assume that

$$x^k - y^k = (x - y)\left(\sum_{u=1}^{k} x^{k-u}y^{u-1}\right).$$

Then,

$$x^{k+1} - y^{k+1} = x^{k+1} - xy^k + xy^k - y^{k+1}$$
$$= x(x^k - y^k) + y^k(x - y)$$
$$= x\left[(x - y)\left(\sum_{u=1}^{k} x^{k-u}y^{u-1}\right)\right] + y^k(x - y)$$
$$= (x - y)\left[x\left(\sum_{u=1}^{k} x^{k-u}y^{u-1}\right) + y^k\right]$$
$$= (x - y)\left[\sum_{u=1}^{k} x^{k+1-u}y^{u-1} + y^k\right]$$
$$= (x - y)\left(\sum_{u=1}^{k+1} x^{k+1-u}y^{u-1}\right).$$

Thus, by a mathematical induction proof we conclude that the statement is true for every positive integer n. In another notation,

$$x^n - y^n = (x - y)(x^{n-1} + x^{n-2}y$$
$$+ x^{n-3}y^2 + \cdots + xy^{n-2} + y^{n-1}).$$

11. For every positive integer n,

$$(\cos \theta)(\cos 2\theta)(\cos 4\theta)(\cos 8\theta) \cdots (\cos 2^{n-1}\theta) = \frac{\sin 2^n\theta}{2^n \sin \theta}.$$

Proof: (1) Since

$$\cos \theta = \frac{2 \sin \theta \cos \theta}{2 \sin \theta} = \frac{\sin 2\theta}{2 \sin \theta},$$

the statement is true for $n = 1$.

(2) Assume that

$$(\cos \theta)(\cos 2\theta)(\cos 4\theta)(\cos 8\theta) \cdots (\cos 2^{k-1}\theta) = \frac{\sin 2^k\theta}{2^k \sin \theta}$$

is a true statement. Thus,

$$[(\cos \theta)(\cos 2\theta)(\cos 4\theta)(\cos 8\theta) \cdots (\cos 2^{k-1}\theta)] \cos 2^k\theta$$

$$= \frac{\sin 2^k\theta}{2^k \sin \theta} \cdot \cos 2^k\theta$$

$$= \frac{2(\sin 2^k\theta)(\cos 2^k\theta)}{2^{k+1} \sin \theta}$$

$$= \frac{\sin 2^{k+1}\theta}{2^{k+1} \sin \theta}.$$

Using the First Principle of Induction, we conclude that the statement is true for every positive integer.

12. *De Moivre's Theorem.* If t is any real number and n a positive integer, then

$$(\cos t + i \sin t)^n = \cos nt + i \sin nt$$

where $i = \sqrt{-1}$.

Proof: (1) The statement is obviously true for the positive integer 1.

(2) Assume that

$$(\cos t + i \sin t)^k = \cos kt + i \sin kt$$

is a true statement. Now,

$$(\cos t + i \sin t)^{k+1} = (\cos t + i \sin t)(\cos t + i \sin t)^k$$
$$= (\cos t + i \sin t)(\cos kt + i \sin kt)$$
$$= (\cos t \cos kt - \sin t \sin kt)$$
$$+ i(\sin t \cos kt + \cos t \sin kt).$$

We use the trigonometric identities

$$\cos A \cos B - \sin A \sin B = \cos (A + B)$$

and $\qquad \sin A \cos B + \cos A \sin B = \sin (A + B)$

and obtain the following:

$$(\cos t + i \sin t)^{k+1} = \cos (t + kt) + i \sin (t + kt)$$
$$= \cos (k + 1)t + i \sin (k + 1)t$$

Since we have shown that

$$(\cos t + i \sin t)^n = \cos nt + i \sin nt$$

is a true statement for $n = 1$ and that it is true for $n = k + 1$ whenever it is true for $n = k$, we conclude that the statement is true for every positive integer.

13. Let c be a real number such that $0 < c \le 1$. If $\{s_n\}$ is a sequence defined inductively by

$$s_1 = \frac{c}{2}, \quad s_{k+1} = \frac{s_k^2}{2} + \frac{c}{2}$$

for $k \ge 1$, then

(a) $s_{n+1} > s_n$ for every positive integer n;

(b) $s_n < 1$ for every positive integer n.

Proof: (a) Part 1. Since

$$s_2 = \frac{c^2}{8} + \frac{c}{2} = \frac{c}{2}\left(\frac{c}{4} + 1\right)$$

and since $(c/4) + 1 > 1$, we have $s_2 > (c/2)$; thus, $s_2 > s_1$.

Part 2. Assume that $s_{k+1} > s_k$. Now, by definition of the sequence,

$$s_{k+2} - s_{k+1} = \left(\frac{s_{k+1}^2}{2} + \frac{c}{2}\right) - \left(\frac{s_k^2}{2} + \frac{c}{2}\right)$$
$$= \frac{s_{k+1}^2 - s_k^2}{2}$$

Since $s_{k+1} > s_k$, we have

$$\frac{s_{k+1}^2 - s_k^2}{2} > 0.$$

Thus, $s_{k+2} - s_{k+1} > 0$ and $s_{k+2} > s_{k+1}$.

Therefore, we conclude $s_{n+1} > s_n$ for every positive integer n.

(b) Part 1. $s_1 = c/2 \le \frac{1}{2} < 1$.

Part 2.   Assume that $s_k < 1$. Thus, $s_k^2 < 1$. Now,

$$s_{k+1} = \frac{s_k^2}{2} + \frac{c}{2}$$

$$< \frac{1}{2} + \frac{c}{2}$$

$$< 1$$

Since $s_1 < 1$, and since $s_k < 1$ implies that $s_{k+1} < 1$, we conclude that $s_n < 1$ for every positive integer n.

14.   For every positive integer n,

$$\sum_{u=1}^{n}(-1)^{u+1}u^2 = (-1)^{n+1}\sum_{u=1}^{n}u.$$

[Note: For $n = 8$, this theorem states that

$$1 - 4 + 9 - 16 + 25 - 36 + 49 - 64$$
$$= -(1 + 2 + 3 + 4 + 5 + 6 + 7 + 8)$$

is a true statement.]

Proof: (1)   Since

$$\sum_{u=1}^{1}(-1)^{u+1}u^2 = 1,$$

and since

$$(-1)^{1+1}\sum_{u=1}^{1}u = 1,$$

the statement is true for $n = 1$.

(2)   Assume that

$$\sum_{u=1}^{k}(-1)^{u+1}u^2 = (-1)^{k+1}\sum_{u=1}^{k}u$$

is a true statement. Then,

$$\sum_{u=1}^{k+1}(-1)^{u+1}u^2 = \sum_{u=1}^{k}(-1)^{u+1}u_2 + (-1)^{k+2}(k+1)^2$$

$$= (-1)^{k+1} \sum_{u=1}^{k} u + (-1)^{k+2}(k+1)^2 \quad \text{(Assumption)}$$

$$= (-1)^{k+2}\left[\left(-\sum_{u=1}^{k} u\right) + (k+1)^2\right]$$

$$= (-1)^{k+2}\left[-\frac{k(k+1)}{2} + (k+1)^2\right] \quad \begin{matrix}\text{(Formula for}\\\text{sum of } k\\\text{integers)}\end{matrix}$$

$$= (-1)^{k+2}\left(\frac{k^2 + 3k + 2}{2}\right)$$

$$= (-1)^{k+2}\frac{(k+1)(k+2)}{2}.$$

Since the sum of the first $(k+1)$ integers is $(k+1)(k+2)/2$,

$$\sum_{u=1}^{k+1}(-1)^{u+1}u^2 = (-1)^{k+2}\sum_{u=1}^{k+1} u.$$

Thus, on the assumption that the statement is true for the integer k, we have proved that it is true for $k + 1$.

The statement is true for every positive integer n.

15. If $\{a_n\}$ is the sequence defined by

$$a_n = \left(1 + \frac{1}{n}\right)^n,$$

then $a_n < 2.79166 \cdots$ for every positive integer n.†

Proof: Using the sum formula for a geometric series (see Problem 7 where $a = 1/2^4$ and $r = \frac{1}{2}$), we have

$$\sum_{u=4}^{n} \frac{1}{2^u} = \frac{1}{2^3} - \frac{1}{2^n}.$$

Hence,

$$\sum_{u=4}^{n} \frac{1}{2^u} < \frac{1}{8}$$

---

† The proof given to show that this sequence is bounded is not the standard two-part induction proof. It is included because it seems to be a new proof of this well-known theorem, it makes use of various other statements already proved, and it makes use of the sigma notation and binomial coefficients. Furthermore, the limit of this sequence is $e = 2.71828\cdots$, the base of the natural logarithms; hence, it is of particular interest in mathematics.

for all n. Adding $(\frac{1}{2!} + \frac{1}{3!})$ to both sides of the inequality,

$$\frac{1}{2!} + \frac{1}{3!} + \sum_{u=4}^{n} \frac{1}{2^u} < \frac{19}{24}.$$

Since $n! > 2^n$ for $n \geq 4$ (see Chapter Two, page 12), $1/n! < 1/2^n$, and we conclude that

$$\frac{1}{2!} + \frac{1}{3!} + \frac{1}{4!} + \frac{1}{5!} + \cdots + \frac{1}{n!} < \frac{19}{24}.$$

Thus,

$$\frac{n(n-1)}{n^2} \cdot \frac{1}{2!} + \frac{n(n-1)(n-2)}{n^3} \cdot \frac{1}{3!}$$
$$+ \frac{n(n-1)(n-2)(n-3)}{n^4} \cdot \frac{1}{4!} + \cdots + \frac{n!}{n^n} \cdot \frac{1}{n!} < \frac{19}{24}.$$

Adding $1 + n(1/n) = 2$ to both sides of the inequality, and noting that, say,

$$\frac{n(n-1)(n-2)}{3!} = {}_nC_3,$$

we get

$$\sum_{u=0}^{n} {}_nC_u \frac{1}{n^u} < 2\frac{19}{24}.$$

Since

$$\left(1 + \frac{1}{n}\right)^n = \sum_{u=0}^{n} {}_nC_u \frac{1}{n^u},$$

we conclude that

$$\left(1 + \frac{1}{n}\right)^n < 2\frac{19}{24} = 2.79166\cdots.$$

16.   If $x_1, x_2, x_3, \cdots, x_n$ are n real numbers in the closed interval $[a, b]$, then the real number

$$\frac{x_1 + x_2 + x_3 + \cdots + x_n}{n}$$

is in the closed interval $[a, b]$; that is,

$$a \leq \frac{x_1 + x_2 + x_3 + \cdots + x_n}{n} \leq b.$$

Proof: (1) For $n = 1$, we have $a \leq x_1/1 \leq b$; this is a true statement, since it is given that x_1 is in the closed interval $[a, b]$.

(2) Assume that

$$a \leq \frac{x_1 + x_2 + x_3 + \cdots + x_k}{k} \leq b.$$

If

$$\frac{x_1 + x_2 + x_3 + \cdots + x_k}{k} \leq b,$$

then $x_1 + x_2 + x_3 + \cdots + x_k \leq kb$. Since $x_{k+1} \leq b$, by adding the inequalities we get

$$x_1 + x_2 + x_3 + \cdots + x_k + x_{k+1} \leq b(k + 1).$$

Thus,

$$\frac{x_1 + x_2 + x_3 + \cdots + x_k + x_{k+1}}{k + 1} \leq b.$$

Similarly, we can prove that

$$a \leq \frac{x_1 + x_2 + x_3 + \cdots + x_k + x_{k+1}}{k + 1}.$$

Consequently,

$$a \leq \frac{x_1 + x_2 + x_3 + \cdots + x_k + x_{k+1}}{k + 1} \leq b.$$

Steps (1) and (2) prove the statement true for every positive integer.

17. Jensen's Inequality. A function f defined on a closed interval $[a, b]$ is called convex if for every pair of numbers y and z in $[a, b]$ we have

$$f\left(\frac{y + z}{2}\right) \leq \frac{f(y) + f(z)}{2}.$$

Prove for any positive integer n that if f is a convex function and $x_1, x_2, x_3, \cdots, x_n$ are numbers in the closed interval, then

$$f\left(\frac{x_1 + x_2 + x_3 + \cdots + x_n}{n}\right)$$
$$\leq \frac{f(x_1) + f(x_2) + f(x_3) + \cdots + f(x_n)}{n}.$$

Proof: (1) [We shall use Theorem 2.4 and show first that the statement is true for every integer n that is a power of 2; that is, we prove first that the statement is true for $n = 2^u$ for every positive integer u. Furthermore, we make use of Problem 16, which states that

$$\frac{x_1 + x_2 + x_3 + \cdots + x_n}{n}$$

is in the closed interval $[a, b]$ for every positive integer n.]

If $n = 2^u$, for $u = 1$ we have $n = 2$ and

$$f\left(\frac{x_1 + x_2}{2}\right) \le \frac{f(x_1) + f(x_2)}{2},$$

which is true, since f is a convex function.

(2) Assume that the statement is true for $u = k$; that is, assume that it is true for the integer 2^k. Thus,

$$f\left(\frac{x_1 + x_2 + x_3 + \cdots + x_{2^k}}{2^k}\right) \le \frac{f(x_1) + f(x_2) + f(x_3) + \cdots + f(x_{2^k})}{2^k}.$$

Now,

$$f\left(\frac{x_1 + x_2 + x_3 + \cdots + x_{2^k} + x_{2^k+1} + \cdots + x_{2^{k+1}}}{2^{k+1}}\right)$$

$$= f\left(\frac{\dfrac{x_1 + x_2 + x_3 + \cdots + x_{2^k}}{2^k}}{2} + \frac{\dfrac{x_{2^k+1} + x_{2^k+2} + \cdots + x_{2^{k+1}}}{2^k}}{2}\right)$$

$$\le \frac{f\left(\dfrac{x_1 + x_2 + \cdots + x_{2^k}}{2^k}\right) + f\left(\dfrac{x_{2^k+1} + x_{2^k+2} + \cdots + x_{2^{k+1}}}{2^k}\right)}{2}$$

$$\le \frac{f(x_1) + f(x_2) + \cdots + f(x_{2^k})}{2^{k+1}} + \frac{f(x_{2^k+1}) + f(x_{2^k+2}) + \cdots + f(x_{2^{k+1}})}{2^{k+1}}$$

$$\le \frac{f(x_1) + f(x_2) + \cdots + f(x_{2^{k+1}})}{2^{k+1}}.$$

Thus, the statement is true for $u = 1$, and we have proved it true for $u = k + 1$ on the assumption it is true for $u = k$. We conclude the statement is true for every positive integral power of 2.

(3) Now, we need only to prove that, if it is true for the integer u, then it is true for $u - 1$. If the statement is true for any u numbers in the interval $[a, b]$, then

$$f\left(\frac{x_1 + x_2 + \cdots + x_{u-1} + \dfrac{x_1 + \cdots + x_{u-1}}{u-1}}{u}\right)$$

$$\leq \frac{f(x_1) + f(x_2) + \cdots + f(x_{u-1}) + f\left(\dfrac{x_1 + x_2 + \cdots + x_{u-1}}{u-1}\right)}{u}.$$

But,

$$f\left(\frac{x_1 + x_2 + \cdots + x_{u-1} + \dfrac{x_1 + x_2 + \cdots + x_{u-1}}{u-1}}{u}\right)$$

$$= f\left(\frac{x_1 + x_2 + \cdots + x_{u-1}}{u-1}\right).$$

Thus, by substitution

$$f\left(\frac{x_1 + x_2 + \cdots + x_{u-1}}{u-1}\right) \leq \frac{f(x_1) + f(x_2) + \cdots + f(x_{u-1})}{u}$$

$$+ \frac{1}{u} f\left(\frac{x_1 + x_2 + \cdots + x_{u-1}}{u-1}\right).$$

Hence, by subtracting the last term from both sides,

$$\frac{u-1}{u} f\left(\frac{x_1 + x_2 + \cdots + x_{u-1}}{u-1}\right)$$

$$\leq \frac{f(x_1) + f(x_2) + \cdots + f(x_{u-1})}{u}.$$

We conclude that

$$f\left(\frac{x_1 + x_2 + \cdots + x_{u-1}}{u-1}\right) \leq \frac{f(x_1) + f(x_2) + \cdots + f(x_{u-1})}{u-1}.$$

By Theorem 2.4, the statement is true for every positive integer.

18. For every positive integer n,

$$\sum_{u=1}^{n} (u)(u!) = (n+1)! - 1.$$

Proof: (1) Since

$$\sum_{u=1}^{1} (u)(u!) = (1)(1!) = 1$$

and since for $n = 1$

$$(n + 1)! - 1 = (2!) - 1 = 2 - 1 = 1,$$

the statement is true for $n = 1$.

(2) Assume that

$$\sum_{u=1}^{k} (u)(u!) = (k + 1)! - 1.$$

Then,

$$\sum_{u=1}^{k+1} (u)(u!) = \sum_{u=1}^{k} (u)(u!) + (k + 1)[(k + 1)!] \qquad \text{(Definition 3.2)}$$
$$= (k + 1)! - 1 + (k + 1)[(k + 1)!] \qquad \text{(Assumption)}$$
$$= [(k + 1)!][1 + k + 1] - 1$$
$$= [(k + 1)!][k + 2] - 1$$
$$= (k + 2)! - 1.$$

As a consequence of the First Principle of Induction, steps (1) and (2) prove that the statement is true for every positive integer n. (If we notice that $(u + 1)! - u! = (u)(u!)$ is a true statement for every positive integer u, then

$$\sum_{u=1}^{n} [(u + 1)! - u!] = \sum_{u=1}^{n} (u)(u!),$$

and the telescoping property of the sigma notation can be used to prove this theorem.)

19. For every positive integer n,

$$\sum_{u=1}^{n} \frac{1}{\sqrt{u}} > \sqrt{u}$$

for $n \geq 2$.

Proof: (1) Since

$$\sum_{u=1}^{2} \frac{1}{\sqrt{u}} = \frac{1}{\sqrt{1}} + \frac{1}{\sqrt{2}} = 1 + \frac{\sqrt{2}}{2},$$

and since $1 + (\sqrt{2}/2) > \sqrt{2}$,[†] we conclude that the statement is true for $n = 2$.

(2) Assume that

$$\sum_{u=1}^{k} \frac{1}{\sqrt{u}} > \sqrt{k}$$

for $k \geq 2$. Then

$$\sum_{u=1}^{k+1} \frac{1}{\sqrt{u}} = \sum_{u=1}^{k} \frac{1}{\sqrt{u}} + \frac{1}{\sqrt{k+1}} \qquad \text{(Definition 3.2)}$$

$$> \sqrt{k} + \frac{1}{\sqrt{k+1}}. \qquad \text{(Assumption)}$$

Our problem is to prove that $\sqrt{k} + (1/\sqrt{k+1}) \geq \sqrt{k+1}$.

Since $\sqrt{k+1} > \sqrt{k}$ for $k \geq 2$, then multiplying by $\sqrt{k}$ we get

$$\sqrt{k}\sqrt{k+1} > k.$$

Thus,

$$\sqrt{k}\sqrt{k+1} + 1 > k + 1$$

by adding 1 to both sides, and

$$\sqrt{k} + \frac{1}{\sqrt{k+1}} > \frac{k+1}{\sqrt{k+1}}$$

by dividing both sides by $\sqrt{k+1}$. Consequently,

$$\sqrt{k} + \frac{1}{\sqrt{k+1}} > \sqrt{k+1}.$$

Thus,

$$\sum_{u=1}^{k+1} \frac{1}{\sqrt{u}} > \sqrt{k+1}.$$

By Theorem 2.2, we conclude that the statement is true for every positive integer $n \geq 2$.

20. Let $\{s_n\}$ be the sequence defined inductively by $s_1 = 1$, $s_2 = 3$, and $s_{k+1} = 3s_k - 2s_{k-1}$ for $k \geq 2$. For every positive integer n, $s_n = 2^n - 1$.

---

† $\sqrt{2} < 2$ implies that $2\sqrt{2} < 2 + \sqrt{2}$; thus, $\sqrt{2} < 1 + (\sqrt{2}/2)$.

Proof: (1) Since $s_1 = 2^1 - 1 = 1$, and since $s_2 = 2^2 - 1 = 3$, the statement is true for the integers 1 and 2.

(2) Assume that $s_t = 2^t - 1$ is true for every integer $t \leq k$. Thus,

$$
\begin{aligned}
s_{k+1} &= 3s_k - 2s_{k-1} \\
&= 3(2^k - 1) - 2(2^{k-1} - 1) \\
&= 3(2^k) - 3 - 2^k + 2 \\
&= 2(2^k) - 1 \\
&= 2^{k+1} - 1.
\end{aligned}
$$

By Theorem 2.3, we conclude that $s_n = 2^n - 1$ for every positive integer n.

MATHEMATICAL INDUCTION
EXERCISES

Chapter Five

The statements (exercises) that are followed by an asterisk are proved in the text.

1.* For every positive integer n,

$$\sum_{u=1}^{n} u = \frac{n(n + 1)}{2}.$$

2.* For every positive integer n,

$$\sum_{u=1}^{n} u^2 = \frac{n(n + 1)(2n + 1)}{6}.$$

3.* For every positive integer n,

$$\sum_{u=1}^{n} u^3 = \frac{n^2(n + 1)^2}{4}.$$

4.　For every positive integer n,

$$\sum_{u=1}^{n} u^4 = \frac{n(n + 1)(2n + 1)(3n^2 + 3n - 1)}{30}.$$

5.　For every positive integer n,

$$\sum_{u=1}^{n} u^5 = \frac{n^2(n + 1)^2(2n^2 + 2n - 1)}{12}.$$

6.　For every positive integer n,

$$\sum_{u=1}^{n} u^6 = \frac{n(n + 1)(2n + 1)(3n^4 + 6n^3 - 3n + 1)}{42}.$$

7.　For every positive integer n,

$$\sum_{u=1}^{n} u(u + 1) = \frac{n(n + 1)(n + 2)}{3}.$$

8.　For every positive integer n,

$$\sum_{u=1}^{n} u(u + 1)(u + 2) = \frac{n(n + 1)(n + 2)(n + 3)}{4}.$$

9.　For every positive integer n,

$$\sum_{u=1}^{n} u(u + 1)(u + 2)(u + 3) = \frac{n(n + 1)(n + 2)(n + 3)(n + 4)}{5}.$$

10.　For every positive integer n,

$$\sum_{u=1}^{n} (2u - 1) = n^2.$$

11.　For every positive integer n,

$$\sum_{u=1}^{n} (2u - 1)^3 = n^2(2n^2 - 1).$$

12.*　For every positive integer n,

$$\sum_{u=1}^{n} \frac{1}{u(u + 1)} = \frac{n}{n + 1}.$$

13. For every positive integer n,
$$\sum_{u=1}^{n} \frac{1}{(3u - 2)(3u + 1)} = \frac{n}{3n + 1}.$$

14. For every positive integer n,
$$\sum_{u=1}^{n} (4u - 3) = n(2n - 1).$$

15. For every positive integer n,
$$\sum_{u=1}^{n} (u^2 + 1) = \frac{n(2n^2 + 3n + 7)}{6}.$$

16.* For every positive integer n,
$$\sum_{u=1}^{n} ar^{u-1} = \frac{ar^n - a}{r - 1}$$
where a and r are real numbers and $r \neq 1$.

17. For every positive integer n,
$$\sum_{u=1}^{n} u(2^u) = 2 + (n - 1)2^{n+1}.$$

18. For every positive integer n,
$$\sum_{u=1}^{n} 2(3^{u-1}) = 3^n - 1.$$

19. For every positive integer n,
$$\sum_{u=1}^{n} [a + (u - 1)d] = \frac{n[2a + (n - 1)d]}{2}$$
where a and d are real numbers.

20.* For every positive integer n,
$$\sum_{u=1}^{n} (-1)^{u+1} u^2 = (-1)^{n+1} \sum_{u=1}^{n} u.$$

21.* For every positive integer n,
$$\sum_{u=1}^{n} (u)(u!) = (n + 1)! - 1.$$

22. For every positive integer n,

$$\sum_{u=1}^{n} (3u^2 - u + 2) = n^3 + n^2 + 2n.$$

23.* For every positive integer $n \geq 2$,

$$\sum_{u=1}^{n} \frac{1}{\sqrt{u}} > \sqrt{n}.$$

24. For every positive integer n,

$$(n - 1)(n)(n + 1)$$

has 6 as a factor.

25. For every positive integer n,

$$(n - 1)(n)(n + 1)(n + 2)$$

has 24 as a factor.

26. For every positive integer n,

$$n^5 - 5n^3 + 4n$$

has 120 as a factor.

27. For every positive integer n,

$$n^5 - n$$

has 5 as a factor.

28. For every positive integer n,

$$\sum_{u=1}^{n} u^5$$

has $n(n + 1)/2$ as a factor.

29. For every positive integer n,

$$2^{2n+1} + 1$$

has 3 as a factor.

30.* For every positive integer n,

$$6^{n+2} + 7^{2n+1}$$

has 43 as a factor.

31. For every positive integer n,
$$4^{n+1} + 5^{2n-1}$$
has 21 as a factor.

32. For every positive integer n,
$$n^3 + (n + 1)^3 + (n + 2)^3$$
has 9 as a factor.

33.* For every positive integer n,
$$n^2 + n$$
has 2 as a factor.

34.* For every positive integer n,
$$x^{n+1} - 1 = (x - 1) \sum_{u=0}^{n} x^n.$$

35.* For every positive integer n,
$$(x + y)^n = \sum_{u=0}^{n} {}_nC_u x^{n-u} y^u.$$

36.* For every positive integer n,
$$x^n - y^n = (x - y) \sum_{u=1}^{n} x^{n-u} y^{u-1}.$$

37. For every positive integer n,
$$x^{2n-1} + y^{2n-1}$$
has $(x + y)$ as a factor.

38. For every positive integer n,
$$x^{2n} - y^{2n}$$
has $(x + y)$ as a factor.

39.* For every positive integer n,
$$\cos n\pi = (-1)^n.$$

40.* For every positive integer n,
$$(\cos \theta)(\cos 2\theta)(\cos 4\theta)(\cos 8\theta) \cdots (\cos 2^{n-1} \theta) = \frac{\sin 2^n\theta}{2^n \sin \theta}.$$

41.* If t is a real number and $i = \sqrt{-1}$, for every positive integer n,
$$(\cos t + i \sin t)^n = \cos nt + i \sin nt.$$

42. For every positive integer n,
$$\sum_{u=1}^{n} \cos (2u - 1)\theta = \frac{\sin 2n\theta}{2 \sin \theta}.$$

43. For every positive integer n,
$$\sum_{u=0}^{n} \cos u\theta = \frac{1}{2} + \frac{\sin (n + \frac{1}{2})\theta}{2 \sin (\theta/2)}.$$

44. For every positive integer n,
$$\sum_{u=1}^{n} \sin (2u - 1)\theta = \frac{\sin^2 n\theta}{\sin \theta}.$$

45.* Let $\{a_n\}$ be the sequence defined inductively by $a_1 = 1$, $a_2 = 2$, and $a_k = a_{k-1} + a_{k-2}$ for $k > 2$. For every positive integer n,
$$a_n < \left(\frac{7}{4}\right)^n.$$

46. Let $\{a_n\}$ be a sequence such that $a_n < a_{n+1}$ for all n. For every positive integer n,
$$\sum_{u=1}^{n} \frac{a_u}{n} < \sum_{u=1}^{n+1} \frac{a_u}{n + 1}.$$

47. Let $\{a_n\}$ be the sequence defined inductively by $a_1 = 1$ and $a_k = \sqrt{3a_{k-1} + 1}$ for all $k \geq 2$. For every positive integer n,
$$a_n < a_{n+1}.$$

48. Let $\{a_n\}$ be the sequence defined inductively by $a_1 = 1$ and $a_k = \sqrt{3a_{k-1} + 1}$ for all $k \geq 2$. For every positive integer n,
$$a_n < \tfrac{7}{2}.$$

49. Let $\{a_n\}$ and $\{b_n\}$ be sequences such that $b_n > 0$ and
$$\frac{a_n}{b_n} < \frac{a_{n+1}}{b_{n+1}}$$
for all n. For every positive integer n,

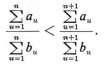

$$\frac{\sum\limits_{u=1}^{n} a_u}{\sum\limits_{u=1}^{n} b_u} < \frac{\sum\limits_{u=1}^{n+1} a_u}{\sum\limits_{u=1}^{n+1} b_u}.$$

50. Let $\{a_n\}$ be a sequence of positive numbers. For every positive integer n,

$$\sqrt[n]{a_1 \cdot a_2 \cdot a_3 \cdots a_n} \leq \frac{a_1 + a_2 + a_3 + \cdots + a_n}{n};$$

that is, the geometric mean is less than or equal to the arithmetic mean.

51*. For every positive integer n,

$$\sum_{u=1}^{n} (a_u + b_u) = \sum_{u=1}^{n} a_u + \sum_{u=1}^{n} b_u.$$

52.* For every positive integer n,

$$\sum_{u=1}^{n} c a_u = c \sum_{u=1}^{n} a_u$$

where c is a real number.

53.* For every positive integer n,

$$\sum_{u=1}^{n} (a_{u+1} - a_u) = a_{n+1} - a_1.$$

54.* Let c be a real number where $0 < c \leq 1$ and let $\{s_n\}$ be the sequence defined inductively by $s_1 = c/2$,

$$s_{k+1} = \frac{s_k^2}{2} + \frac{c}{2}$$

for $k \geq 1$. Then

(a) $s_{n+1} > s_n$ for every positive integer n;

(b) $s_n < 1$ for every positive integer n.

55.* Let $\{a_n\}$ be the sequence defined by $a_n = [1 + (1/n)]^n$. For every positive integer n,

$$a_n < 2.79166\cdots.$$

56.* If $x_1, x_2, \cdots, x_n$ are n real numbers in the closed interval $[a, b]$, then

$$a \leq \frac{x_1 + x_2 + x_3 + \cdots + x_n}{n} \leq b$$

for every positive integer n.

57.* Let $\{s_n\}$ be the sequence defined inductively by $s_1 = 1$, $s_2 = 3$, and $s_{k+1} = 3s_k - 2s_{k-1}$ for $k > 2$. For every positive integer n,

$$s_n = 2^n - 1.$$

58. Let $\{a_n\}$ be the sequence defined inductively by $a_1 = 1$, $a_2 = 2$, and $a_{k+2} = a_{k+1} + a_k$ for $k \geq 1$. For every positive integer n,
$$a_{n+1}^2 - a_n a_{n+2} = (-1)^{n+1}.$$

59. Let $\{a_n\}$ be the sequence defined inductively by $a_1 = 1$, $a_2 = 2$, and $a_k = a_{k-1} + a_{k-2}$ for $k > 2$. For every positive integer n,

$$\sum_{u=1}^{n} a_{2u} = a_{2n+1} - 1.$$

60.* Given a line segment of unit length, for every positive integer n, a line segment of length $\sqrt{n}$ can be constructed by straightedge and compass.

61.* For every positive integer $n \geq 4$,
$$2^n < n!.$$

62. For every positive integer $n \geq 3$, the number of diagonals in a convex polygon with n sides is $n(n - 3)/2$.

63.* For every positive integer $n \geq 2$, the number of lines obtained by joining n distinct points in the plane, no three of which are collinear, is $n(n - 1)/2$.

64.* For every positive integer n,

$$\frac{n^5}{5} + \frac{n^3}{3} + \frac{7n}{15}$$

is an integer.

65. For every positive integer n,
$$\frac{n^7}{7} + \frac{n^3}{3} + \frac{11n}{21}$$
is an integer.

66. For every positive integer $n > 9$,
$$n^3 < 2^n.$$

67. For every positive integer n,
$$n^7 < 7 \sum_{u=1}^{n} u^6.$$

68. For every positive integer n,
$$\frac{n^n}{e^n} < n!$$
where $e = 2.71828\cdots$.

69. For every positive integer n,
$$(2 + \sqrt{3})^n + (2 - \sqrt{3})^n$$
is an integer.

70. For every positive integer n, the number of subsets of a set with n elements is 2^n.

71.* For every positive integer n, if $0 < x < 1$, then
$$0 < x^n < 1.$$

72.* Let f be a convex function defined on a closed interval $[a, b]$ and let $x_1, x_2, x_3, \cdots, x_n$ be n numbers in the closed interval. For every positive integer n,
$$f\left(\frac{x_1 + x_2 + x_3 + \cdots + x_n}{n}\right)$$
$$\leq \frac{f(x_1) + f(x_2) + f(x_3) + \cdots + f(x_n)}{n}.$$